How TO BE BRAVE

Written by Danielle Jones

Illustrated by Yury Borgen

To my biggest fans, Jason, Braxton and Beckett. I love you.

"You are my sun, my moon and all my stars."- E.E. Cummings.

Special thanks to Yury Borgen for your amazing illustrations, book layout and design.

Do you know what it means to be brave?

Being brave takes courage,

and it's not always easy.

It means that you show courage

even when faced with adversity,

and bravery comes in many different forms.

Be brave enough to help others when they need it.

Be brave enough to try something new,

even if it scares you.

Be brave enough to do what's right.

Be brave enough to be different,

even though it might mean you're judged for it.

Being different takes being brave!

Being different is OK!

Be brave enough

to explore new things.

Be brave enough to welcome someone new.

We were all new at one point.

EMERGENCY EXIT

Be brave enough to explore the unknown.

Be brave enough to do something that scares you.

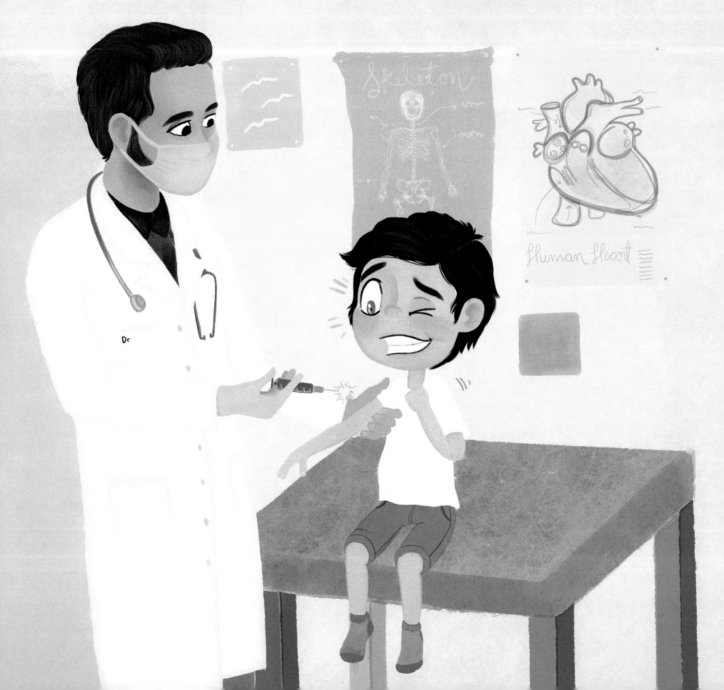

Be brave enough to show your emotions.

We all have emotions,

and it's OK to show them!

Be brave enough to be responsible and clean up your own messes instead of pushing blame on someone else or pretending it didn't happen.

Be brave enough to show determination and not give up.

Be brave enough to know you won't always have everything figured out,

and that's OK!

Be brave enough to ask for help!

Be brave enough to stand up for a friend.

You'll never know when you might need a friend

to do the same for you.

Be brave enough to cheer on others.

Be brave enough to dream BIG!

No dream is TOO big!

Be Brave
enough
to be
YOU!

Sometimes being brave can be scary,

and that's OK!

If you feel like what you're doing is right,

then you're being brave!

Made in the USA
Las Vegas, NV
04 October 2021